HOW IT WORKS...
TELEVISION

by DAVID CAREY
with illustrations by B. H. ROBINSON

Ladybird Books Loughborough

Introduction

The television set is a familiar piece of equipment in homes throughout the world. At the turn of a switch we can sit and watch things that are happening many miles away. Without moving from our chairs we can see plays and shows transmitted from special studios, we can be spectators at exciting sporting events, and by means of radio links, we can be transported in sound and vision to many different countries. It is all so comfortable and easy that we take it completely for granted as part of our everyday lives.

Television is one of the marvels of our age, yet how many children, or adults for that matter, ever stop to wonder how it works? If you do, this book is for you. It explains the various principles on which the whole system is based and how the major parts are designed to make use of those principles. It also describes how a programme is put on, how outside broadcasts are tackled and many of the other details that go to make up the spare time occupation we call viewing.

It all began in 1922, in a bedroom of a Hastings boarding house. John Logie Baird, a Scotsman, was the inventor. He used a washstand as his work bench and his odd assortment of equipment included an old electric motor, two cycle lamp lenses, a torch, parts of a disused radio, wire, string, glue, and sealing wax. But we have progressed a very long way from that day, as you will see.

7214 0130 9

13. Scenery storage (basement)
14. Receiving aerial mast
15. Scenery runway serving all studios
16. Scenery entrance to Studio Three
17. Restaurant Block
18. Lift and Ventilation plant

19. Studio Eight and accommodation for BBC Television News (Under construction)
20. Telerecording rooms (below ground level)
21. East Tower
22. Car Park

Under construction

Series 654

Television is one of the marvels of our age, yet how many people ever stop to wonder how it works? If you do, this book is for you. It explains the various principles on which the whole system is based and how these principles are used to give us so many hours of enjoyable viewing at home.

A careful text and excellent full-colour illustrations are an encouragement to learn all one can from this book.

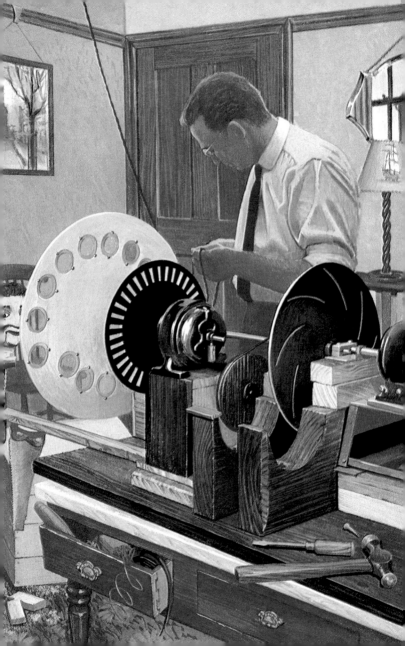

What is Television?

Television is the transmission and reception of images of moving objects by radio waves. Although it is indeed one of the marvels of our age, its operation is not quite as difficult as you might think. But it does involve the use of certain principles which we must understand before we can appreciate how a picture with its sound can be sent from one place and viewed in another.

The word 'television' is a combination of Greek and Latin words. The Greek word 'tele' means 'at a distance' and it is used in other forms of long distance com-munication such as *tele*gram and *tele*phone. Vision comes from the Latin 'video', meaning 'I see'.

Television starts wherever the event we wish to see is taking place. The action is made into a picture by the television camera which then turns it into electricity. The electricity is changed into radio-frequency power which is then sent out by a transmitter in the form of radio waves. These set up tiny electrical currents in the aerial on the roof of your home, which are conducted down into your receiving set where they are amplified and changed into a picture again.

The whole process happens so quickly that you can see the action at home at almost precisely the same time that it is occurring elsewhere. Also, you see on your screen exactly what the camera sees in the studio, or wherever it is. Programmes are sometimes recorded for showing at another time, and we often see films on a variety of different subjects. All these are part of modern television and you will learn how they are dealt with as you read through the book.

Principles of the Television Camera

When you look at a 'live' (not a pre-recorded) programme, the picture you see on your screen at home begins in a television camera. This is an electronic device for making a picture and turning that picture into electricity.

There are various types of television cameras in use today, each operating in a slightly different way, but all designed to do the same job. Some of the newer ones are rather complicated, but the general principles can be understood if we examine an early type. To make it easier we shall describe its action step by step.

The television camera is not like an ordinary film camera. It does not take a complete picture of a scene. What it does is to break the picture up into a series of lines consisting of tiny points of light following one another at very high speed. The variations of tone between the dark and light areas are represented by points of light of varying shades of grey.

Look at a picture in a newspaper. It appears to be a complete picture. Now look at the same picture through a magnifying glass. You will see that it is made up of hundreds of little dots. Very broadly speaking, a television picture is made up in the same way, except that the dots consist of many thousands of tiny points of light which vary in intensity according to the brightness of the scene.

What we have to do now is to find out how the points of light are made and how each one is turned into an electrical impulse, so that it may be sent to you through space.

Turning the Picture into Electricity

A television camera has to look at a scene and change the light and dark that it sees into minute charges of electricity.

Behind the camera lens is a screen, or *mosaic*, covered with thousands of tiny dots of a material known as caesium. The dots are so close together that the mosaic appears to be coated all over with caesium but, in fact, the dots are completely separated from each other. Caesium is a substance which has the special property of being *photo-sensitive*, and each caesium dot is what is known as a miniature *photo-electric cell*. This means that when light falls on the dots they release *electrons*, or, in other words, generate small charges of electricity.

When the camera lens is pointed at a scene, the picture it sees is focussed on to the mosaic screen and the dots of caesium release electrons, i.e. become charged with electricity. The number of electrons, and therefore, the amount of electricity generated, depends on the strength of the light falling on each caesium dot. A bright light releases more electrons and produces a stronger electrical charge from each dot. A dull light releases fewer electrons and produces a weaker electrical charge from each dot. In this way the lighter parts of the picture being televised will release more electrons, while the darker portion will release less electrons. The variations in picture tone are thus translated into variations in the electrical charge being generated by the different caesium dots. The whole picture entering the camera is, therefore, turned into an identical 'picture' made up of varying electrical charges.

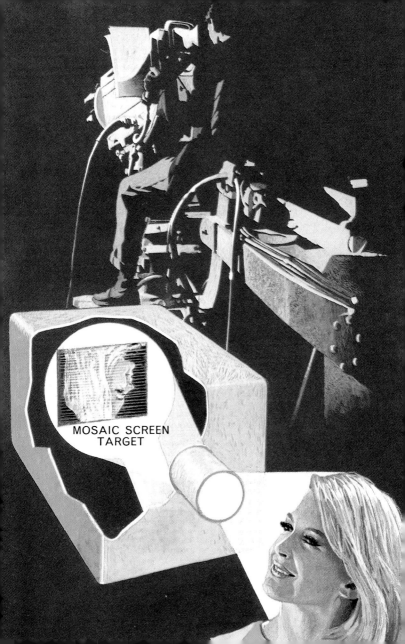

MOSAIC SCREEN
TARGET

The Electron Gun

The electrical charges in the caesium dots cannot be released without help. The next step is to get each tiny charge to set up electrical *currents* which can be amplified (made stronger) and transmitted as *electro-magnetic radio waves* to our television aerials.

This is done by the *electron gun*. It is a device which shoots out a stream of electrons in the form of a needle-like beam, rather like a machine-gun shooting out bullets, only much faster. Magnetic deflector coils, or plates, are placed around the muzzle of the gun and, by adjusting the electrical current flowing through them, the gun can be aimed in such a way that its beam sweeps back and forth, and also up and down, across the mosaic screen. The movement of the electron beam is the same as that of your eyes when you read this book—from left to right. This sweeping action is known as *scanning*.

The electron beam scans the whole mosaic screen fifty times every second, releasing the various electrical charges from all the caesium dots as it passes over them. These charges of current are then sent through an amplifier to make them stronger, and eventually transformed into electro-magnetic radio waves which radiate from the transmitting aerial. Just as the electrical charges in the dots are large or small according to the amount of light that has fallen on them, so the electron beam produces a large or small change of electrical current as it scans the dots.

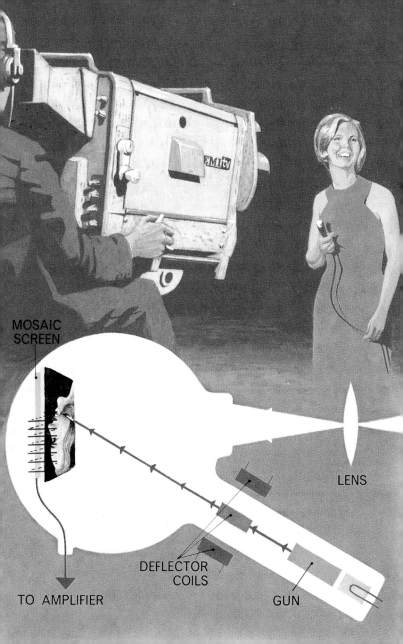

MOSAIC
SCREEN

LENS

DEFLECTOR
COILS

GUN

TO AMPLIFIER

What is Sound ?

Whilst the television camera is picking up the picture, we must have some means of picking up the voices of the actors or commentators and all the other sounds connected with the scene being televised. The camera's job is to turn the *picture* into electricity: the microphone's job is to turn the *sound* into electricity. Before we see how the microphone does this, there are certain principles we must first know about.

All sounds are the result of vibrations which travel through the air in waves. You can feel sound vibrations by placing your hand over your open mouth and saying 'ah'. The little tingle in your hand is caused by the *vibrations* of the sound you are making. A loud sound is the result of powerful vibrations which in turn cause powerful waves. A soft sound is the result of weak vibrations which, therefore, produce weak waves.

Different kinds of sounds are the result of different sorts of vibration. If something vibrates frequently, that is—a great many times per second, it produces a *high-frequency* sound. We hear it as a high-pitched noise like a squeak, a whistle or a scream. On the other hand, something vibrating slowly produces a *low-frequency* sound. It has a low pitch which is heard as a low note like a growl, a groan or a very deep voice.

Sound waves can travel only a certain distance. A loud noise, causing powerful waves, will travel further than a soft noise, but even powerful sound waves will not travel far enough for us to hear a noise if we are a long way from the object or person making it. The normal human ear will hear vibrations from about sixteen per second to about sixteen thousand per second.

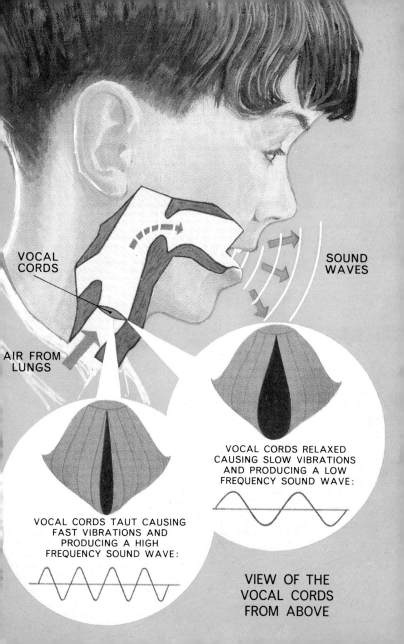

VOCAL
CORDS

SOUND
WAVES

AIR FROM
LUNGS

VOCAL CORDS RELAXED
CAUSING SLOW VIBRATIONS
AND PRODUCING A LOW
FREQUENCY SOUND WAVE:

VOCAL CORDS TAUT CAUSING
FAST VIBRATIONS AND
PRODUCING A HIGH
FREQUENCY SOUND WAVE:

VIEW OF THE
VOCAL CORDS
FROM ABOVE

More about Sound Waves

We can illustrate the movement of sound waves quite simply by studying something we have all done at some time—dropping a stone into a pond.

A stone dropped into a smooth pond causes little ripples—or waves—to radiate out from the centre. The ripples continue to move outward, causing less and less disturbance to the surface of the pond as they get further away from the spot at which the stone was thrown in. Eventually they disappear altogether, leaving the pond perfectly smooth again. A big stone will cause big ripples which will travel much further across the pond before they disappear.

Sound waves travel in a similar manner to the ripples on the pond. A loud noise, like a big stone, will cause a bigger disturbance which will travel further. Just as the water was necessary to carry the ripples, so must air—or a liquid or some solid material—be present to carry sound waves. If something vibrates and there is no air or liquid or solids to carry the sound waves, we do not hear the sound. It would be useless to shout for help in Space because, even if someone was near enough to help, there is no air to carry the vibrations. Astronauts 'walking' in space have to speak to one another by means of two-way radio. Electro-magnetic radio waves do not need air to carry them: they travel better without.

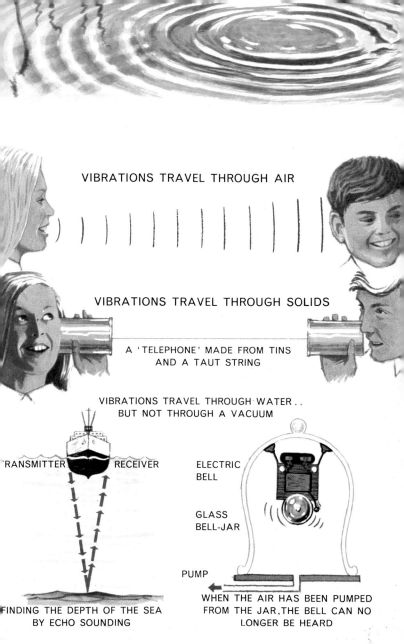

VIBRATIONS TRAVEL THROUGH AIR

VIBRATIONS TRAVEL THROUGH SOLIDS

A 'TELEPHONE' MADE FROM TINS
AND A TAUT STRING

VIBRATIONS TRAVEL THROUGH WATER..
BUT NOT THROUGH A VACUUM

TRANSMITTER   RECEIVER

ELECTRIC
BELL

GLASS
BELL-JAR

PUMP

FINDING THE DEPTH OF THE SEA
BY ECHO SOUNDING

WHEN THE AIR HAS BEEN PUMPED
FROM THE JAR, THE BELL CAN NO
LONGER BE HEARD

How a Microphone Works

We have seen that a sound travels through air by vibrations. If an ear is in the path of the sound wave, it sets the ear drum vibrating and the sound is heard. A microphone is a kind of electric ear. In it, in place of the ear drum, we have a thin metal plate called a diaphragm which is set in vibration by the sound. The diaphragm is part of the microphone equipment which is designed to transform the mechanical vibration into an electrical one.

The microphones used in the studios are nearly all 'Ribbon', 'Moving Coil' or 'Electrostatic'. In the ribbon type the metal diaphragm is a very thin aluminium ribbon clamped in the gap of a strong magnet. As the sound wave vibrates the ribbon, the movement of the ribbon in the field of the magnet creates an alternating electrical voltage across the ends of the ribbon.

In the moving coil type, a thin metal diaphragm is attached to a coil in the radial magnetic field of a circular magnet. When a sound wave causes the diaphragm to vibrate, the coil vibrates also, and cuts the magnetic field at right angles. This also produces an alternating voltage at the terminals of the coil.

In each case, the electrical output of the microphone is an *alternating voltage*, varying in strength and frequency as does the original sound, and which can be amplified and fed to a transmitter and/or a loudspeaker.

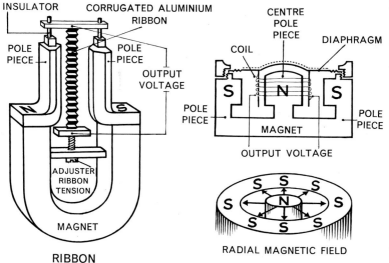

INSULATOR · CORRUGATED ALUMINIUM RIBBON

POLE PIECE · POLE PIECE

OUTPUT VOLTAGE

N · S

ADJUSTER RIBBON TENSION

MAGNET

RIBBON MICROPHONE
(cover removed)

CENTRE POLE PIECE · DIAPHRAGM

COIL

S · N · S

POLE PIECE · POLE PIECE

MAGNET

OUTPUT VOLTAGE

S S S
S N S
S S S

RADIAL MAGNETIC FIELD

MOVING COIL MICROPHONE

Electro-Magnetic Waves

What have we learned so far? We know that a picture can be converted into changes of electricity by means of the television camera, and that sounds can also be converted into changes of electricity by using a microphone. So we have two kinds of electrical changes; one on the vision, or *video* side and the other on the sound, or *audio*, side. We now have to find a way of sending these varying electric currents through the sky to all the homes waiting to receive them. But to understand how this is done we shall have to go back to some more basic principles.

Sound waves travel only as far as we can hear them. Light also travels in waves which are restricted by what we can see with our eyes. Neither of these waves are much use when we are trying to see and hear things that are going on many miles away. The transmission of sound and pictures was made possible with the discovery of the *electro-magnetic radio wave*, and this is the means by which we transfer the variations of electric current (produced by camera and microphone) from the transmitting aerial to the receiving aerial.

The electro-magnetic radio wave does not need air, water or solid material in order to radiate. One occasion when an electro-magnetic wave is created is when a spark jumps between any two electrical points. The wave it sends out will appear as a spot on your television screen or as a crackle on your radio. You can see and hear this happen when you switch off an electric light or fire, or when a motor car (with its sparking plugs not correctly suppressed) is running nearby, or when an electric bell rings.

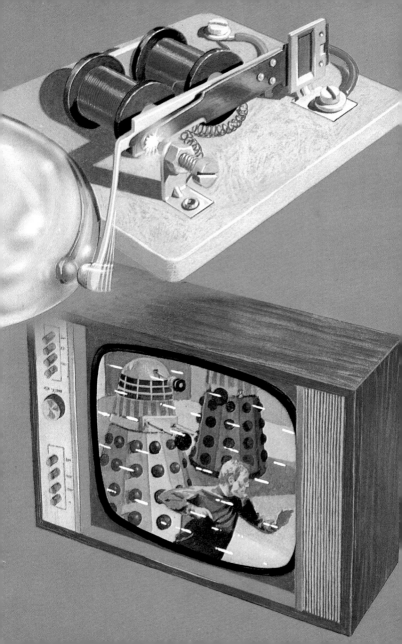

The Electro-Magnetic Carrier Wave

Although electro-magnetic waves are, of course, invisible, they are in many ways like the ripples on the pond: they die away unless they can be kept going by some means. Radio and television transmitters are able to create continuous electro-magnetic waves (though, of course, by other means than sparking), and these travel outwards from the transmitting aerial like the ripples on the pond—only *continuously*.

We mentioned earlier that sound waves have a *frequency*. The alternating electric current used in our homes for lighting and heating also has a frequency (fifty cycles per second), which means that the current is flowing first in one direction and then back again, in a sort of alternate backward and forward movement. Electro-magnetic waves also flow backward and forward—or *oscillate*, and each backward and forward movement is known as a *cycle*. Radio frequencies vary from thousands to millions of cycles per second.

Now if a coil of wire in which electro-magnetic energy is oscillating is connected through a transmitting set to an aerial on a tower or mast, electro-magnetic waves will continuously radiate from the tower. These continuous electro-magnetic waves are called the *carrier wave*, and it is on this carrier wave that the vision and sound signals from the television camera and the microphone are carried to our homes.

It is essential that the carrier wave is much higher in frequency than the sound or television signal it must carry.

FLOW OF ALTERNATING CURRENT IN A WIRE

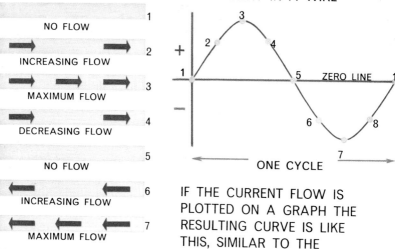

NO FLOW — 1

INCREASING FLOW — 2

MAXIMUM FLOW — 3

DECREASING FLOW — 4

NO FLOW — 5

INCREASING FLOW — 6

MAXIMUM FLOW — 7

DECREASING FLOW — 8

ONE CYCLE

IF THE CURRENT FLOW IS PLOTTED ON A GRAPH THE RESULTING CURVE IS LIKE THIS, SIMILAR TO THE RIPPLES ON THE POND.

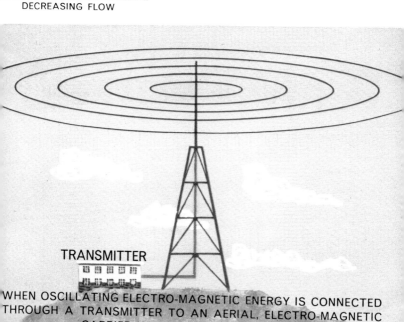

TRANSMITTER

WHEN OSCILLATING ELECTRO-MAGNETIC ENERGY IS CONNECTED THROUGH A TRANSMITTER TO AN AERIAL, ELECTRO-MAGNETIC CARRIER WAVES ARE TRANSMITTED.

Transmitting the Programme

As we have seen, the carrier wave which is generated at the transmitter consists of a *continuous* flow of waves *of the same strength*, or *amplitude*. As we have also seen, the sound to be transmitted is first picked-up by the microphone, in which the diaphragm vibrates according to the frequency of the sound waves striking it. These vibrations cause changes in the electric voltage coming from the microphone. In order to transmit the sound, these changes must then be mixed with the carrier wave, causing variations in its amplitude, or strength. A loud sound at the microphone will then cause a big variation, and a soft sound a small variation, in the amplitude of the carrier wave. This mixing with the carrier wave is known as *modulation*, and the variations in amplitude, according to the sound being broadcast, is known as *amplitude modulation*.

Changes in the electrical current made by the electron gun in the T.V. camera are dealt with in the same way. In their case it is not sound waves but the tiny light dots which cause the current changes. These changes are mixed with another carrier wave and make their own amplitude modulations. We therefore have sound and vision represented by changes in amplitude of electro-magnetic carrier waves, ready to be picked-up by thousands of household aerials all over the country. And because these waves travel at the speed of light (one hundred and eighty-six thousand, two hundred and eighty-two miles per second) we all see and hear the programme at almost the precise time that it is being enacted.

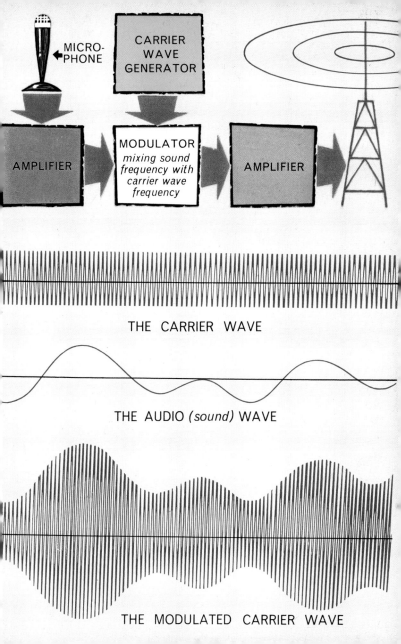

MICRO-PHONE

CARRIER WAVE GENERATOR

AMPLIFIER

MODULATOR
mixing sound frequency with carrier wave frequency

AMPLIFIER

THE CARRIER WAVE

THE AUDIO *(sound)* WAVE

THE MODULATED CARRIER WAVE

Receiving the Sound

As the electro-magnetic waves sent out by the transmitter are radiated from the aerial, they travel outwards—sometimes in all directions, but often beamed in certain desired directions. To receive them, we must put a receiving aerial in the path of these modulated waves.

On meeting the aerial, if this is tuned to the frequency of the carrier, a voltage varying at the carrier frequency, and similarly modulated, will be created in the aerial, and the resultant current can be fed down a special cable to a television receiver.

The job of the sound side of the television set is to recover, from the high frequency sound carrier wave, the original sound variations. It would be useless to connect the sound carrier signal direct to a loudspeaker. Even if a loudspeaker could be made to react to such high frequencies, our ears would hear nothing.

The received radio frequency signal is passed through a 'rectifier'—a sort of one way valve or crystal. This rectifier passes all the *positive* half-cycles of the radio wave, but suppresses the negative half-cycles. This leaves all the positive half-cycles, which are varying in amplitude at the audio rate, as a pulsating one way current. This pulsating signal is passed (through smoothing circuits which suppress the high frequency carrier variations) to an amplifying valve producing an electrical output at the original audio frequency. This is now fed to the input terminals of a loudspeaker, the cone of which vibrates according to the variations of the electrical current fed to it. The vibrations of the cone send out sound waves which we hear as the sound which went into the microphone many miles away.

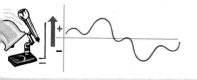

THE OUTPUT OF A
MICROPHONE IS AN
ALTERNATING VOLTAGE

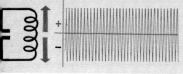

THE CARRIER WAVE IS ALSO
ALTERNATING BUT AT A
MUCH HIGHER FREQUENCY

THE MODULATED CARRIER
WAVE. THIS IS ALSO
POSITIVE AND NEGATIVE

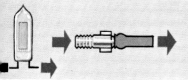

THE RECTIFYING VALVE
ALLOWS CURRENT TO GO
ONLY ONE WAY JUST AS THE
BICYCLE VALVE ALLOWS AIR TO
PASS ONLY ONE WAY

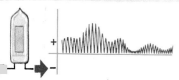

AFTER GOING THROUGH THE
RECTIFIER THE MODULATED WAVE
IS NOW ONLY POSITIVE, BUT STILL
VARYING. THE NEGATIVE HALF-
CYCLES HAVE BEEN SUPPRESSED

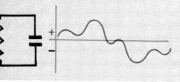

SMOOTHING CIRCUITS ELIMINATE
THE HIGH FREQUENCY CARRIER
AND LEAVE ONLY THE ORIGINAL
AUDIO FREQUENCY

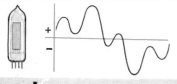

THE AMPLIFYING VALVE MAKES
THE VOLTAGE STRONGER

THE STRONGER VARYING CURRENT
PASSES THROUGH TO THE
LOUDSPEAKER WHICH THEN
REPRODUCES THE ORIGINAL SOUND

Receiving the Picture

We read on page twenty-four that the changes in electric current caused by the sound reaching the microphone were transmitted on a carrier wave, and that also the modulations made by the changes of electric current produced in the television camera were carried by another carrier wave.

The waves induced in the aerial by the carrier wave transmitting the picture pass down the receiving aerial to the television set, where they also pass through a rectifying valve. *As with the sound side*, the oscillating movement of the electro-magnetic waves is converted in the rectifier into a one-way flow of current changes. These are amplified to give them greater strength and then fed into the cathode-ray tube of the T.V. set. We now have the same kind of current changes going into the receiver that came away from the camera. Big changes of current representing the white specks in the camera, and small changes of current representing the dark specks.

One end of the cathode ray tube has an electron gun similar to that in the television camera. At the other end of the tube is a fluorescent screen—the screen on which we see the picture. It is called fluorescent because the inside of the glass is coated with a special fluorescent material which gives off rays of light when electrons are shot onto it by the electron gun. This material covers the screen in the form of thousands of tiny particles. Each particle gives off a speck of light of which the brightness depends on the number of electrons reaching it.

Special devices in the transmitter and receiver keep the receiver scanning beam exactly in step with the television camera's scanning beam.

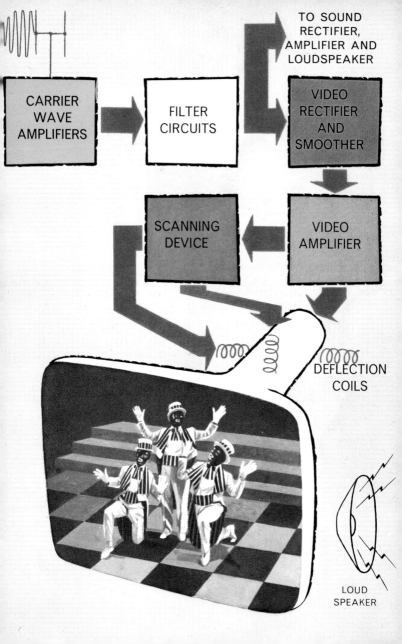

TO SOUND
RECTIFIER,
AMPLIFIER AND
LOUDSPEAKER

CARRIER
WAVE
AMPLIFIERS

FILTER
CIRCUITS

VIDEO
RECTIFIER
AND
SMOOTHER

SCANNING
DEVICE

VIDEO
AMPLIFIER

DEFLECTION
COILS

LOUD
SPEAKER

How the Cathode-Ray Tube Works

As mentioned in the previous chapter, the changes of current for the picture to be received are separated from the carrier wave by a rectifier, amplified and fed into the electron gun at the back of the cathode-ray tube. They cause the gun to shoot out a needle-like beam of electrons. A big change in current produces a greater number of electrons, a small change in current produces less electrons.

The gun scans the fluorescent screen at the viewing end of the tube from left to right and top to bottom, exactly in step with the scanner in the television camera. As the electrons strike the tiny specks of material they glow for an instant. Big changes in current produce more electrons which give a brighter light speck. Small changes in current produce fewer electrons which give a duller light speck on the screen. This exactly reverses what happens in the camera, where it is the dots of light from the picture that cause changes of current. And so the scene originally picked up by the camera is faithfully reproduced on the television screen. Light portions of the scene become light portions on the screen, dark portions of the scene become dark portions on the screen.

You can now perhaps understand that the whole process of television consists of breaking up a picture into tiny specks of light, converting the specks into big and small changes of electric current, sending the changes of current in the form of electro-magnetic waves through the air, converting them back into specks of light and finally arranging the specks in the original pattern to form the picture again. What the camera sees at the transmission end, your television screen shows, speck for speck, at the receiving end.

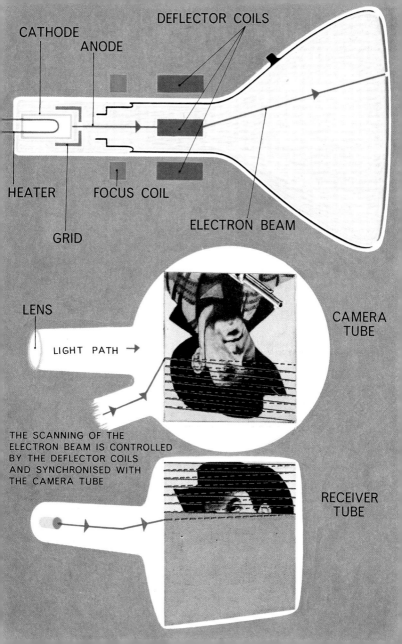

DEFLECTOR COILS

CATHODE

ANODE

HEATER

FOCUS COIL

GRID

ELECTRON BEAM

LENS

LIGHT PATH →

CAMERA TUBE

THE SCANNING OF THE
ELECTRON BEAM IS CONTROLLED
BY THE DEFLECTOR COILS
AND SYNCHRONISED WITH
THE CAMERA TUBE

RECEIVER TUBE

A Picture that is not really there

Although we now know how a picture is brought to our television screens, there are still one or two important facts to be explained. Firstly, we must understand that the picture we see is not really there at all! If we could slow everything down sufficiently we would find that, at any given fraction of a second, there is only one tiny speck on the screen. It would be the speck of fluorescent material being hit by the electron beam at that instant. In other words, the picture is built up of thousands of tiny specks of light appearing one at a time. It is only because the electron beam is scanning the screen at such a fantastic speed, plus something known as *persistence of vision*, that we see what appears to be a complete picture.

B.B.C.1 and I.T.A. pictures are made up of 405 lines. This means that the electron beam scans across the screen in 405 lines from top to bottom. It does this 25 times every second. It scans the odd lines first; 1, 3, 5, 7, 9, 11 and so on up to $202\frac{1}{2}$ lines. It then switches back to the top of the screen and covers the lines it has left out, i.e., 2, 4, 6, 8, 10, etc. In this way it forms two *interlacing frames* of $202\frac{1}{2}$ lines each, making up the full number of 405.

Persistence of vision, mentioned above, is a normal feature of human eyesight. In connection with television it means that although the spots of light are continually going on and off, our eyes cannot detect the split-second intervals and think the spots are there all the time.

IF YOU DRAW THESE TWO PICTURES OF A LITTLE GIRL
ALTERNATELY THROUGHOUT THE PAGES OF A NOTE BOOK,
SHE WILL APPEAR TO BE SKIPPING WHEN THE PAGES ARE
FLIPPED OVER QUICKLY. PERSISTENCE OF VISION BETWEEN
PICTURES WILL MAKE THE ACTION SEEM CONTINUOUS.

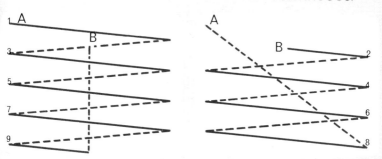

FIRST HALF ODD LINES   SECOND HALF EVEN LINES

(FOR DIAGRAMMATIC REASONS, ONLY A FEW LINES ARE SHOWN ABOVE)

DIAGRAM OF INTERLACED SCANNING

Wavelengths and Frequencies

Electro-magnetic waves can be measured in terms of wavelengths or frequencies. To understand these measurements we can go back to the pond and the ripples. When the stone is dropped into the water the little ripples, or waves, radiate out from the centre. The distance between the top of one wave to the top of the next one to it is the *wavelength*. The number of waves that radiate out from the centre every second is the *frequency*.

Translating this back into electro-magnetic waves, the top of one wave to the top of the next is the wavelength. Take a look at the tuning dial on a radio set. The figures marked on the dial indicate the wavelengths on which the various stations are transmitting their programmes. Each station must have its own different wavelength, so that the different programmes can be picked up separately and not become jumbled one on top of another. For instance, the B.B.C. Radio 2 Programme is transmitted on a long wavelength of 1500 metres. This tells us that the distance between the top of one wave to the top of the next is 1500 metres.

Frequency is measured in cycles per second. A cycle is one backward and forward movement of the alternating current which makes the electro-magnetic waves. High-frequency is a lot of cycles per second, low-frequency is fewer cycles per second.

Frequency $\times$ Wavelength = Speed of Light (186,282 miles per second). Therefore, high-frequency goes with a short wavelength and low-frequency goes with a long wavelength because electro-magnetic waves always travel at the speed of light.

It is usual to refer to low frequencies in terms of wavelengths, and to the high-frequencies in terms of frequency.

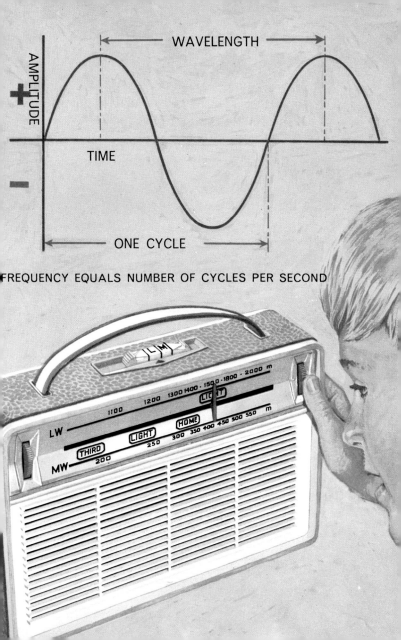

WAVELENGTH

AMPLITUDE

+

−

TIME

ONE CYCLE

FREQUENCY EQUALS NUMBER OF CYCLES PER SECOND

Television Networks
and Transmitting Aerials

The long wave section of an ordinary wireless uses a sound carrier of around 200,000 cycles per second (wavelength = 1,500 metres). Medium wave stations use a carrier of about 1,500,000 cycles per second (wavelength = 200 metres). For television sound, the sound carrier frequency has to be near to the very high frequency of the vision signal carrier (because both must be receivable by the same aerial), thus the frequency of the television sound carrier in the 405 line system is 150,000,000 cycles per second (wavelength = 2 metres).

All radio waves spread outward from the transmitter in straight lines. Because the earth is round, one would expect reception of a radio wave would only be possible within sight of the transmitter. Fortunately the upper atmosphere has a number of ionised layers (conglomerations of electric charges) which reflect the radio waves, particularly at night, like a mirror reflects light. The returning waves are again reflected by the earth, and the waves can travel very long distances in a series of hops—in fact, right round the earth.

Unfortunately the *very* short wavelengths used for television are not so well reflected by the ionised layers; so, to cover the whole country, a large number of transmitters have to be used.

Transmitting stations can be set up within receiving distance of each other and a programme can be sent from one to another and then passed on to the next.

There is now a network of transmitters all over Europe, and we can sometimes see, in our own homes, events that are actually happening in other countries. The satellite 'Telstar' is another form of television relay station. It amplifies and reflects the signals it receives from transmitters on one side of the Atlantic and thus relays them to the other side.

Transmitting masts are usually set on high ground in open country, and can be of steel girder or cylindrical steel construction.

N.E. SCOTLAND : DURRIS

N.E. ENGLAND : BURNHOPE

N. ENGLAND : EMLEY MOOR
one of the new cylindrical masts
which are the tallest in EUROPE

N. IRELAND : STRABANE

MIDLANDS : LICHFIELD

N. WALES : MOEL·Y·PARC

CHANNEL ISLANDS

The Television Studio

All live television programmes, other than outside broadcasts, start in the television studio. This is a big enclosed area, rather like a film studio. It has a large amount of permanent equipment. Big, powerful lights are mounted on galleries high up near the roof, and there are mobile lights that can be moved to different positions on the floor. A television production needs a great amount of lighting.

Cameras are required, and one studio may have several of these, mounted on different kinds of stands. Some stands are fixed while others have wheels to enable the cameras to be pushed to various positions. Nearly every studio will have one camera mounted on an electrically-operated crane which is used to take high-angle and moving shots. Microphones are needed to give us the sound. There are several different kinds of these. There is the fixed type for talks and quiz shows, where it does not matter if the microphone is seen in the picture. There are microphones which can be carried in the hand or hung round the neck of the performers to enable them to move about while they are talking or singing. Then there is the boom microphone which we should never see on our screens. It hangs on the end of a boom, or beam, over the heads of the actors and can be swivelled and moved to catch the sounds in a play or other action where the sight of the microphone would spoil the effect.

A studio is also provided with a number of *sets* which can be built up to make backgrounds and scenes for various shows.

Controlling the Show

Every television studio has a control room with a large sound-proof glass window set above the studio floor and over-looking the action that is taking place. In here sit the producer with his assistants, and the programme engineers. .

The producer is in radio contact with the studio floor managers and the cameramen, and he can give them instructions during the programme on telephone head-sets they are wearing. In front of him are several monitor screens which show him the scene being 'shot' by each of the cameras. Another monitor shows him the picture that is actually being transmitted. Several cameras are used in each television show and they can be moved to various sets and scenes, and their outputs can be selected as required. The producer has to see that the camera, microphone, actors and sets are always ready for the next scene before the previous one ends. By watching the studio action and monitor screens, he can switch over to the right camera at the right time and give the *cue* to get the new scene going. The different camera positions, and the places where the performers must stand, are chalked on the floor during rehearsals, so everyone knows where to go.

The programme engineers keep an eye on the picture quality from each camera and an ear to the sound from the microphones. If these were not carefully balanced we should have to keep adjusting our T.V. sets for every new scene.

Outside Broadcasts

A television programme that does not come from a studio is known as an Outside Broadcast. There are three main kinds of outside broadcasts; those arranged by the television company (visits to a theatre, a zoo, a circus and so on); those in which the cameras are taken to a special event (in this group we have all the sporting broadcasts, a royal wedding, important speeches); and thirdly, the mobile transmissions which we shall be dealing with in the next chapter.

As in studio transmissions, several cameras are normally used for an outside broadcast. One camera is probably arranged so that it takes in the whole scene and shows the complete field of action. Unfortunately, because our television screens are rather small, this often means that individual details are not seen very clearly. Another camera is therefore used to show close-up pictures of what is happening, and others may be positioned elsewhere to give several different viewpoints. The producer sites the cameras in the most suitable positions before the event takes place and watches the camera outputs through monitor screens while they are in operation. He can then switch from one camera to another during the broadcast to give the best possible coverage of the event.

The commentator sits with his microphone, usually near one of the cameras, overlooking the scene. He also has a monitor in front of him showing him the same picture we see at home. His commentary is based partly on what he can actually see of the event and partly on what he sees on his monitor screen.

Mobile Transmissions

The portable or mobile transmitters which have to be used for most outside broadcasts are not powerful enough to send a picture directly into our homes. This means that the programme has first to be sent to a permanent transmitter which relays the picture and sound waves to our own sets. There are two ways of doing this. The programme can be sent by *coaxial* cable, or land line as it is often called. This is a direct link by wire connected between the mobile and permanent transmitters.

Alternatively, the programme can be sent by television waves in the usual way, but there is a snag to this. You will remember that television waves can only travel in straight lines. This means that the mobile transmitter aerial must be within sight of the permanent transmitter aerial. This is not always possible because a tall building or hillside might be in the way. In such a case an extra aerial must be erected on the building or hill to provide the extra link necessary to 'bend' the waves and give them their unobstructed path from one transmitter to the other.

The third type of outside broadcast, mentioned in the previous chapter, concerns small micro-wave equipment complete with cameras, microphones, transmitter, etc., which can be carried in a medium-size vehicle. It is a television station in miniature on wheels. The camera can be mounted on the roof of the vehicle and televise a moving scene. This type of equipment is often used to follow horses in a race, cars in a rally and in any event where the camera has to keep up with things that are moving along, and where heavy equipment is unsuitable.

Televising Films and Tape Recordings

So far we have dealt with the transmission of purely 'live' programmes—programmes televised at the same time that they are actually being performed. However, a great many programmes we see on our screen come from cinematograph films, telerecorded films or videotape (magnetic recordings of the vision and sound signals).

Films are often reproduced by using an ordinary cinematograph projector to shine the moving picture on to the target of a television camera, but several other systems are also used. In these a special projector called a 'telecine' projector is used. The projection lamp in the ordinary projector is replaced in the telecine version by a bright screen across which a flying spot is scanned as in a television receiver. In this way the film is scanned by a light beam as it goes through the projector. Behind the film is a kind of electric eye, called a photo-electric cell, which collects the light after it has passed through the film. The light and shade of the film modulates the beam, and the output of the photo-electric cell therefore takes the place of the output from the camera and, when transmitted to our home screen, faithfully recreates the picture.

Recordings of live programmes can be made on film by photographing the picture shown on a television screen. Alternatively, the television signal can be accurately recorded on a special kind of magnetic tape, very like the tape on a home magnetic sound recorder, but two inches wide. In either case the sound is recorded on the same film or tape, on a separate track.

35 mm PROJECTOR

16 mm PROJECTOR

SLIDE PROJECTOR

EMI

VIDEO TAPE MACHINE

Some special effects

The production of television programmes has now reached a high pitch of efficiency. We can enjoy live action, recordings and films in a succession of shows lasting for many hours. What perhaps some of us do not know is that very often we see live action and film all mixed up in the one programme.

Studio productions are limited for space and for the type of sets that can be built. Outside scenes are difficult to reproduce and a car chase through city streets or round country lanes just cannot be done. For this reason many of the plays we watch are a combination of live action in the studio for indoor scenes, and filmed action for outdoor scenes. It is the producer's job to see that the studio shots and telecine sequences are cut in and out at just the right moments to make up a smoothly-running complete production. He usually does it so well that we cannot tell when one finishes and the other begins.

Some musical shows, particularly 'pop' shows and those that involve a lot of movement, are *mimed*. In these, the artistes do not actually make any sound at all. A recording of the music or song is played and the singers pretend to sing by making the miming movements with their mouths.

How are titles (called 'captions') made to move across the screen? It is really very easy. The words are put on to a caption roller which is something like a window blind. Someone winds the handle and they pass across the front of the camera. Upward or sideways, depending on the effect the producer wishes to get.

The introduction of Colour Television

Earlier in this book it was explained that BBC 1 and ITA television programmes are transmitted on the 405 line system. The electron beam scans across the screen that number of times from top to bottom. BBC 2 uses 625 lines, and the extra lines help to give a smoother appearance to the picture.

Soon, colour television will be going into more and more homes. A very brief indication of how this works might be interesting.

In lights, the primary colours are red, blue and green, and, by mixing these lights in correct proportions, light of any shade can be matched. In colour television, light from the scene is collected by a lens on to a set of special mirrors, which reflect light of a given colour but allow through other colours. In this way the light from the scene is split up into its components of red, blue and green and these are taken to separate camera tubes which produce signals for each of these colours.These are processed to produce three separate signals defining the brightness, hue and saturation of the scene. These three signals are broadcast on one carrier wave.

At the receiving set, the three signals are separated and processed to reproduce the signals for the red, green and blue, and these are applied to three guns in one cathode ray tube in which the screen is made up of thousands of phosphoric dots, one-third of which emit red light, one-third blue light and the remaining third green light.

The dots are arranged in groups of three — one of each colour. Between the screen and the dots is a perforated metal mask, the perforations being exactly aligned with the centres of each triangular group of three dots. By this means it is ensured that the red gun only fires at red dots, the blue gun only at blue dots and the green gun at green dots. Thus the scene is reproduced in its true colours.

MIRROR FILTERS

RED

YELLOW

GREEN   WHITE   BLUE

BLUE-
GREEN

THE PRIMARIES AND
THEIR COMBINATIONS

BLUE

GREEN

RED

SHADOW
MASK

BBC TELEVISION CENTRE

1. Studio One
2. Studio Two
3. Studio Three
4. Studio Four
5. Studio Five
6. Studio Six
7. Studio Seven
8. Central Control Room
9. Presentation Studios
10. Scenery Block
11. Carpentry and Machine Shop (ground floor)
12. Set building space (ground floor)

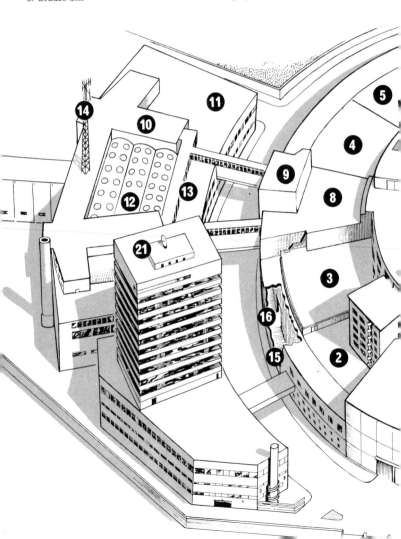